PEANUTS®

Look and Find®

Merry Christmas, Charlie Brown

ILLUSTRATED BY CHARLES M. SCHULZ CREATIVE ASSOCIATES

phoenix international publications, inc.

WHEN CHARLIE BROWN GOES SKATING, HIS DOG SNOOPY JOINS IN, TOO. SEARCH THROUGH THE SKATERS TO FIND SOME OF THEIR WINTER WEAR.

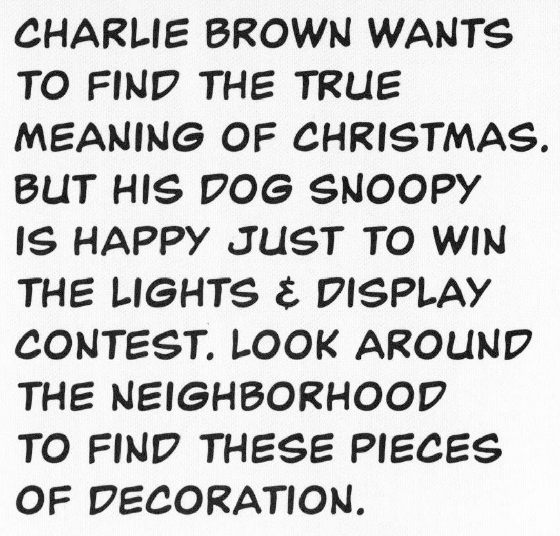

CHARLIE BROWN WANTS TO FIND THE TRUE MEANING OF CHRISTMAS. BUT HIS DOG SNOOPY IS HAPPY JUST TO WIN THE LIGHTS & DISPLAY CONTEST. LOOK AROUND THE NEIGHBORHOOD TO FIND THESE PIECES OF DECORATION.

1st

WHEN CHARLIE BROWN NEEDS MONEY TO BUY PEGGY JEAN A PRESENT, HE DECIDES TO SELL HIS COMIC BOOK COLLECTION. SEARCH THROUGH THE STACKS TO FIND SOME OF CHARLIE BROWN'S OLD FAVORITES.

FOR SALE
USED COMIC BOOKS
LAFF
HUMOR
FUN
FUNNY
HUMOR
LAFF
FUNNY
LAFF
HUMOR
LAFF
HUMOR
HUMOR
COMIC
COMIX
COMIX
FUNNY
Fun!
COMICS
LAFF

"THIS LITTLE GREEN ONE HERE SEEMS TO NEED A HOME," SAYS CHARLIE BROWN. LOOK FOR SOME OTHER CHRISTMAS TREES THAT ARE MUCH MORE COLORFUL.

MARCIE AND PEPPERMINT PATTY GO ON A FIELD TRIP TO HEAR A SYMPHONY. SEARCH THE CROWD FOR THESE MISPLACED INSTRUMENTS.

GIFTS
SALE
NOW
Scarves
"LOOK! I JUST BOUGHT THIS NEW PAIR OF GLOVES!" SAYS PEGGY JEAN. CHARLIE BROWN'S PLAN IS RUINED. SHOP AROUND THE STORE TO FIND SOME GLOVES HE CONSIDERED BUYING FOR PEGGY JEAN.
Gifts

GIFTS
Perfume
SALE
SPECIAL

TIME TO DECORATE THE TREE! LOOK THROUGH THE BOX TO FIND THESE CHRISTMAS ORNAMENTS.

EVERYONE IS HAVING FUN IN THE SNOW! HUNT HIGH AND LOW TO FIND THESE SNAZZY ACCESSORIES FOR THE SNOWMEN.

RETURN TO THE ICE-SKATING PARTY TO FIND THESE KIDS.
GO BACK TO THE LIGHTS & DISPLAY CONTEST TO FIND THESE COLORFUL CANDY CANES.
GO BACK TO THE COMIC BOOK SALE TO FIND THESE OTHER THINGS THAT CHARLIE BROWN TREASURES.
ST PAUL
RETURN TO THE CHRISTMAS TREE LOT TO FIND CHARLIE BROWN'S CHRISTMAS TREE AND THESE OTHER PLAIN AND SIMPLE THINGS.

SOAR BACK TO THE SYMPHONY TO FIND THESE KIDS IN THE AUDIENCE.
• A BOY IN A RED SHIRT SITTING NEXT TO A GIRL WITH CURLS
• A GIRL IN A POLKA-DOTTED DRESS TALKING TO A BOY IN A BLUE SHIRT
• A GIRL IN A BLUE DRESS SITTING NEXT TO TWINS
• A BOY IN A PLAID SHIRT SITTING IN FRONT OF A GIRL IN A GREEN DRESS
• A BOY IN A GREEN SWEATER SITTING NEXT TO A GIRL WITH A PURPLE HAT
• A GIRL IN A PURPLE SHIRT SITTING BETWEEN TWO BOYS
RETURN TO THE DEPARTMENT STORE TO FIND THESE COLORFUL BOTTLES OF PERFUME.
ROLL BACK TO THE BOX FULL OF CHRISTMAS ORNAMENTS TO FIND THESE FESTIVE STICKERS.
HO HO HO
RETURN TO THE SNOW DAY TO FIND SOME FAMILIAR-LOOKING SNOW SCULPTURES.